FAMOUS SEX COMICS

FAMOUS SEX COMICS

By John J. Reynolds, M.A.
Foreword by C. Leslie Lucas, Ph.D.

SOCIO LIBRARY
PAPERBACK BOOKS

First Printing, *December 1971*
Second Printing, *February 1973*
Third Printing, *July 1975*
Fourth Printing, *March 1976*

ISBN 0-87978-621-3

PRINTED IN THE UNITED STATES OF AMERICA

TABLE OF CONTENTS

LIST OF COLOR COMIC STRIPS 7

FOREWORD 9

INTRODUCTION 15

Chapter One
LITTLE PSYCHOLOGICAL TIME CAPSULES 21

Chapter Two
MASS PRODUCTION FOR PSYCHOLOGICAL NEEDS 33
"A NIGHT IN PARIS" 38
"KISS ME AGAIN" 43
"HOT NUTS" 53
THE FULLER BRUSH MAN 78
OPHELIA PRATTE 83
COLONEL BEAUREGUARD GOOSEOIL 88
CONNIE CLAPP 93
"HELP WANTED" 98
THE FULLER BRUSH MAN 107
FORESKIN CUNTWELL 112
JESSIE JAMES 129
BOOBS 134
THE RADIO SALESMAN 150
KANSAS CITY KITTY 155
THE FULLER BRUSH MAN 160
LAPPO 165
DILDO DOOLEY 170
THE FRIGIDAIRE SALESMAN 175
PIERRE LA DOUCHE 185

Chapter Three
REFLECTIONS OF CHANGING ATTITUDES 195

CONCLUSION 213
BIBLIOGRAPHY 215

LIST OF COLOR COMIC STRIPS

THE FULLER BRUSH MAN IN "HOT PANTS".. 48

MISS ANNIBELLE IN "DRINK UP"...........180

FOREWORD

Vision fades. Imagination conquers, and reality becomes bearable. Pain is forgotten. Memories that are fondly recalled deal with love, affection, success, the dream come true, and the gratification of fantasies.

We cherish memories through childhood, puberty, adolescence, and into young adulthood. These recollections strengthen our basic identity, add a sense of security to our lives, and strengthen the core of our existence. Bad memories create pain, ill feelings, and agony. So we do constantly seek the means to find and build on pleasant memories, and to recall those motivations that produced them. This formula of nostalgia has sustained our culturization process down through the centuries.

Recently there have come to light several hundred artifacts that trigger nostalgia. These small eight-page folios beguiled and amused the adolescents and adults of the middle 1930s. They were the little "dirty" comics that burst upon the scene in 1934, and flourished until the wave of upheaval of the Second World War buried them. Originals are now collector's items, commanding fancy prices. They were over-priced even by today's standards. When they first appeared, they cost around five dollars for each folio.

They are eagerly sought by students of American primitive folk art, and by behaviorists who enjoy the camp quality of their artistic style, the naivete of the captions, and the simplicity of story lines. This, coupled with their exercises in humor, forms a fascinating commentary on American social attitudes of the middle decades of this century.

In their heydey they poured forth in quantities that reach around a half million copies per issue, and had a bootlegged type of circulation.

Starring in the "eight-pagers" were such daily establishment comic-strip favorites as: Ella Cinders, Popeye and Olive Oyl, Maggie and Jiggs, Toots and Casper, Dixie Dugan, Harold Teen, Dick Tracy, Moon Mullins, Blondie and Dagwood, Tillie the Toiler and Max, Dumb Dora, Sappo, Boob McNutt, Wimpy, Mickey Finn, Joe Palooka, Major Hoople, The Webbs, the Katzenjammers, Uncle Phil, and others. The daily and Sunday popularity of some of these characters has gone on for decades. In the established press they lived rather asexual lives, and reflected the white, middle class, Anglo-Protestant, and conservative society.

In the southwest and along the West Coast the little dirty comics were often dubbed "Tijuana bibles." It was widely rumored that they were published there. But the rumor is conceded to have been a ruse to deflect the energies of customs agents, and law enforcement officers seeking to suppress this commerce.

It is generally thought that most publication centered in New Jersey, Illinois, and the midwest. Some flourished in California areas.

Our interest here focuses upon the social climate in which they flourished. They parodied the hypocritical standards inherited from the Victorian era. The standards had emerged from a Puritanical code that took root in the Colonial times here in the United States. They are still strongly entrenched in our society today.

The Sunday comics, and their daily continued strip, were similar to the soap opera, but not as involved in daily disasters. Sunday strips sought to reflect an innocent sex appeal, and to provoke a smile about daily life in the presumed average American home. Some strips provided buffoons to give the reader a sense of superiority. Some were appealing from the standpoint of accepted sexual aggression.

They were yesteryear's equivalent of the TV soap opera. As such they offered a rich opportunity for devastating parody. This came about in 1934 with the appearance of the first "eight-pagers." They satisfied the public's appetite for voyeurism and for immediate identification with the marvelous athletic prowess of the established public figure. "Nothing succeeds like success" was one of the constant themes of the little "dirty" comics.

Anatomical accuracy was not the order of the books. Exaggeration was essential. Women's breasts were depicted as more than ample. Women's genitals were inviting, always aquiver with anticipation, and later agitated with satisfaction. Male genitalia were shown with erections of fantastic length, thickness rivaling at least the forearm, and a bulbing head that would best be described as formidable by any standards.

The orgasm was usually reached by frame five, and often repeated in frame eight. The ecstasy revealed rivaled the description in the Kama Sutra. The energy expended was shown as being something close to a mild attack of epilepsy. Occasionally the ejaculation was shown. The productive output of seminal fluid released was similar to the milk output of a dairy cow.

It can be safely and conservatively stated that each page of the little "dirty" comics was generously supplied with sex and comedy. The "eight-pagers" pricked our fantasies by appealing to our sexual interests and our vigorous senses of humor. These books were American Primitive art at the top of its pre-pop-art form. They have been called "sexy vulgarity" and "pictorialized erotica" by such diverse people as Bill Blass and Dr. Evelyn Hooker.

They filled the need for a healthy outlet of sexual fantasizing. The "eight-pagers" were geared to the heterosexual market. They did advocate a great deal of effective foreplay, fellatio, and cunnilingus. But they concentrated overwhelmingly on coitus. There are some with erotic sequences involving lesbianism, but usually a male was present and participating. There was almost no male homosexual activity depicted. When such incidents were utilized they were for the humor of "any-port-in-a-storm," the substitution for the lacking female presence to assuage an essential satyriasis. This attitude is reflected in teenage sexual practices today.

Women were well shaped, clothed in the latest fashions, and displaying such attributes as full breasts, well-rounded hips, long seductively sexy legs, cleavage, perfectly coiffed hair, a hat at a rakish angle, and a twinkle of sexual availability in their expressions.

For the most part, men were not presented as being at all sexually provocative. Usually they were short, often fat, sometimes typical hay-seed or hillbillie types. As often as not they were homelier than the boy-next-door type, which is an American ideal. But they had a sexual athleticism unmatched in the world of actuality. Their appeal was on a facade of seeming innocence, and a lack of beauty and sexual allure. But in frame two and three, when the disrobing began, they emerged as sexual beings of more than heroic proportions and capacities. What a figure to identify with.

The little "dirty" comics were able to prick the bubble of a set of delusions about the virtue of American mores. They parodied the entire social mores of the establishment attitudes. Any study of these newly fashionable comics yields the most succinct grasp of American social attitudes on sex, and sex education of the middle third of this century.

Viewed from the behaviorist attitude they reveal a fascination with size, performance, transitory sexual encounters, quick gratification, as opposed to lasting relationships. They are a most fertile field for the study of American humor, adding to the lexicon of American slang.

Most important, they are still healthy outlets for sexual fantasies, for anyone who has a capacity to be moved by the main stream of Americana and to exercise an innate, typically American sense of humor.

C. Leslie Lucas, Ph.D.
October, 1971
Los Angeles, California

INTRODUCTION

In the year 1906, Edouard Cartailhac and the abbe Henri Breuil revealed to the world an amazing discovery uncovered by a local young boy who was herding goats. He had found a cave, sealed for thousands of human generations, containing some of the most magnificent paintings ever produced by the hand of man. Hidden from the world for more than twenty thousand years, and brought to our awareness only through accident, were highly stylized representations of the extinct fauna of a bygone age. They had been executed by artists whose talents rivaled those of Leonardo and Michelangelo.

These paintings in the cave at Altamira are now open to public view, closely guarded by the Spanish Government. But not all of the cave is open to public display. Certain areas, probably for reasons of safety, are restricted to the surveillance of only specialists in the arts and sciences. And there, in the hidden recesses, another type of drawing can sometimes be found. These are less carefully rendered. Most are little more than stick figures, of the type little children draw when first introduced to pencils and paper. Yet they show a closer kinship between us and the forgotten Cro-Magnards who drew them than do all the magnificent panoramas of thundering bison herds that decorate the outer cave wall.

They are, if you accept such a term in reference to any work of art, "dirty" drawings. They depict men and women in the acts of sexual intercourse.

We cannot know the original intent of the artists who drew them. But we do know that though separated from us by hundreds of centuries in time, they were men like us, with the same appetites that drive us today, and that sex was an important factor in their daily lives. We can also surmise that the sexual acts held some special significance, that they had already become something more than a natural, recreational process openly accepted by all members of the tribal group. Were this not the case, they would, in all likelihood, have received the same sort of artistic attention as did the animal scenes. Clearly, sex had already been relegated to a special place in their thoughts. We can even guess that the society which produced these paintings was, in some ways, sexually repressed; the drawings are stiff, stilted, utterly lacking in humor. And humor in sexual art generally is the product of a society emerging from a period of sexual repression.

Representations of humans engaged in sexual acts can be placed in three general categories (excluding categorization on the basis of artistic skill): (1) totally representational, depicting people with normal organs and involved in relatively normal acts; (2) drawings obviously designed to titillate and arouse, involving individuals (often with outsize genitalia) engaged in those acts which the particular societal group considers, at least openly, to be of a "perverted" nature; and (3) those in which, regardless of whether or not the representations are of unusual acts, or involve remarkable sexual feats, the patent objective of the artist is to express humor through his sexual representations.

Our primary concern is with the last category and, specifically, with the rash of such art that appeared in America during the Depression and declined with the Second World War. We do have erotic comic art today, but it is of an entirely different genre, and is the product of a different philosophy and way of life.

Peak production of these "eight-pagers," as they were then called, was in the depression years. They were turned out by the thousands in garages, the back rooms of dingy stores, any nook or cranny where a small press could be set up and an unemployed artist could be found who was willing to work long hours for small reward. And they had to be artists of some ability, for the subjects of their efforts were the figures familiar to all Americans through the medium of their daily newspapers. The characters had to so closely resemble those they were based on, that no viewer could fail to identify them (indeed, there is considerable cause to believe that a few of the best of these "eight-pagers" were turned out, for their personal amusement, by the same artists who conceived and executed the original comic strips on which they were based).

Of course, not all the artists engaged in producing these erotic versions of the old comics were men of great skill, and quite a few of those that survive, particularly from the end of the period, are badly done, hacked out to meet commercial deadlines. The small, personally operated enterprises became profitable and evolved into commercial operations of some size. Many of the "eight-pagers" were produced by men who misunderstood the reasons for their popularity, assuming that they genuinely represented an erotic release for the sexually perverted. To these men, accuracy of representation was of secondary importance. The characters in these works are often barely recognizable, or else are new characters, dreamed up for the purpose by the creating artists. But the best of these erotic comics were art in the genuine sense, and we can accept them today as comparable to the best cartoon art that has been produced.

It is difficult, in a more sexually enlightened period, to explain the hold these erotic comics had on the popular imagination. And let it not be supposed that only a small part of the general population came into contact with them. Many millions were produced over the years, and although the price was high for the times (ranging from fifty cents to as much as two dollars, an exceedingly large sum during the depression years), they were common articles of exchange in every grade school and high school across the land. Many young boys and girls were brought to their first awareness of the purposes to which the human genitalia could be put by these little books, and they may well have been a factor in the sexual revolution which began shortly after the Second World War. The generation that emerged from that war had been thoroughly exposed to these erotic comics during their school days.

For many of these young men and women, the "eight-pager" was their first introduction to the humorous and the ludicrous in relation to sexual acts. The vision of Popeye battering down a door with his enormous penis probably enlivened the wet dreams of many an adolescent boy, without involving him in a situation where he could genuinely identify with the central character.

Other well known comic characters were central to the themes of the "eight-pagers." Dagwood and Andy Gump, Dixie Dugan and Tillie the Toiler, these and dozens of others, enacted the sexual fantasies of America's children in ways outside the bounds of even juvenile imaginative fancies. And in this exaggeration lay their particular appeal. They were genuinely funny.

The buyers of these erotic wonders have now gone elsewhere. The amorous adventures of Andy Gump no longer tickle their fancies—except as curiosa, memorabilia of a bygone age close behind us in time, but as far removed philosophically as those men of the Cro-Magnon race, who left their erotic stick figures emblazoned on the walls of their caves, to mystify and amuse us.

Chapter One

LITTLE PSYCHOLOGICAL
TIME CAPSULES

What makes a phrase, a concept, a situation "funny" is impossible to define. The humor of one society will often completely escape another. There are individuals to whom humor does not exist; they can see nothing amusing in any situation and cannot understand the reaction of others to an amusing act. As Sigmund Freud pointed out in *Wit and its Relation to the Unconscious*, the creation of humor is not a universal human attribute, nor is the ability to perceive it necessarily that common.

If any generalization can be made defining what is funny to most people, it is that the humorous situation must present a commonplace activity in some new and startling manner, but without in any way threatening the physical or emotional integrity of the viewer or subject. Thus the clown's pratfall amuses us because we know it is not injurious to him. The pie in the face delivered by the film performer is funny—because it is delivered with aplomb, its recipient either deserves it or reacts in the proper manner. And it is, after all, a pie, messy but soft, and incapable of damaging anything but the ego of the recipient.

The humor of the "eight-pager" is in the same category. Although the acts performed were only rumors to most of the juveniles of the period, they were acts sternly forbidden. Sex was dirty, evil, in that time and place. But whereas actual photographs of real people engaged in the remarkable sexual antics depicted might have disturbed psyches unprepared for them, the black-and-white line drawings of the erotic comics were several levels of association removed from reality. Not even the most naive juvenile believed in the reality of Major Hoople, or Wimpy. While Alley Oop's amorous pursuit of a terrified brontosaur (a lost "eight-pager," dimly remembered from the days of the author's youth) might incite in the breast of a young reader an interest in the girl next door, it was hardly calculated to send him questing an experience in bestiality. The portrayed situation was too ludicrous, Mr. Oop's outsize sexual weapon too far beyond the bounds of possibility, for even the most impressionable youth not to see the humor inherent in the situation.

And so it was with most of the other erotic comics of the period. The star performers were not *real* people. They were merely flights of escapist fantasy whose day-to-day antics provided only the contrast by which they could judge and evaluate the real world. In this sense, the "eight pager" not only amused, it provided a juvenile source of sex education in a society wherein all other rational means were lacking. Our present generation of teenagers would probably find them purile. The principal appeal of the "eight-pager," today, is to those adults in their forties, fifties and sixties to whom they were the first graphic introduction to anything approaching the realities of sex.

To fully understand their appeal, these works must be studied against the background that produced them. Victorianism still held sway in American sexual attitudes. The roaring part of the Roaring Twenties was participated in by only a very small percentage of American society. Most people still believed that the less a boy or girl knew about sex the better off they were. It was assumed that a man and a woman would learn all they needed to know between the sheets, on their wedding night. And a surprising number of virgin brides went to the nuptial bed totally unaware of the mechanics of intercourse.

Not all the sexually ignorant were women. In the middle strata of society, the only mode of sexual release open to most unmarried men was the prostitute—and not all employed her. Chastity was a common state, as was sexual ignorance which the chaste life insured.

Today, we educate our children in sexual matters through the schools, through books (such as the Herder and Herder publication, *The Sex Book*) and even, although only to a mild degree, through the television medium. Our boys and girls know what the sex organs look like, what they are evolved for, how they are used in intercourse and what the consequences are of those uses. We had only the little dirty comics. And despite the impossible dimensions of the organs represented, and the amazing uses to which they were sometimes put, we gleaned from these comics some few grains of valid sexual knowledge. The humor inherent in them made this possible. Unfortunately, even the best of the modern sex education books intended for juvenile use strenuously avoid any suggestion of humor in connection with a sexual act. Life is real and earnest in these works; humor is not yet acceptable in juvenile sex fare.

In that regard, the older generation may have been better off than the present. We knew, through our perusal of the erotic comics, that sex could be funny—and we knew through the reactions of the characters that it was supposed to be enjoyable. Snuffy Smith and the Katzenjammer Kids were obviously getting a bang out of their sexual adventures.

Were they generally available today, the little dirty comics would probably not sell well. Those who purchase erotic material for sexual titillation have far stronger fare available in the form of books, magazines, stage plays and motion pictures. And our younger sexually mature have gone on to erotic comic entertainment of another type altogether. Some authorities feel that humor could be properly revived in the field of juvenile sex education. Perhaps the ideal introduction to sex for children before the age of puberty might be an erotic version of *Peanuts*. Can we envision an aroused Snoopy in hot pursuit of his little avian friend?

But the purveyors of the "eight-pagers" were profit, not education oriented. Whatever the reason for their phenomenal success, the publishers were interested in profits. They ground out the most popular versions in enormous quantities and at minimal cost. Unfortunately, they kept the cost down by using the cheapest possible stock, and few copies have survived the decades of handling in condition to be read, much less reproduced for present publication. Press runs ran into the many thousand copies and profits were high. Retail prices ran as high as two dollars for a booklet which cost, in those depression days, as little as a cent or two to produce.

Oddly enough, little dirty books did not face the intense governmental opposition of present erotic publications. They appeared in a less sophisticated society, in which official attitude was more on the order of "let's ignore them and maybe they'll go away." And this despite the fact that a far larger percentage wound up in the hands of juveniles than do present erotic publications, which are written for and sold to an adult market. It was a time in which do-gooders preferred to make believe sex did not exist. And, after all, these make-believe sex cartoons were too unrealistic to threaten the Victorian fortress of social standards.

As previously cited, artistic quality varied

greatly. Surprisingly, it was generally far higher in the early days of the "eight-pager" than in its twilight days; but by that time, the nature of the business had changed and the product acquired a totally different orientation.

The first dirty little comics to appear were actual extensions of the situations appearing in the legitimate comic strips they aped, which appeared daily in the newspapers of America. The characters maintained their customary associations with one another, but they carried the situations into sexual areas. If Little Orphan Annie became sexually engaged, it was with her boon canine companion, Sandy. The characters of Gasoline Alley still had their humorous adventures, but penises and vaginas were brought into play. Also, plot line was adhered to. A rational development of the situation was required. The characters did not immediately jump into the sack with each other, but approached the sexual situation through a rational, if brief, story line.

This situation did not endure. Probably by reason of popular demand, the preliminaries were soon dispensed with and the action joined in the first or second drawing. The artist's objective became to present the maximum of varied erotica in the space allotted. We have seen the same trend in erotic publications currently published for the adult market. The frills have been stripped away and only the inner core of sexuality left to adorn the pages. Humor has been replaced by constant and direct sexual action. Fortunately, even the abruptness with which raw sex was introduced could not destroy the inherent humor of the "eight-pager." The incongruity of the situations depicted preserved them from that fate.

The language, too, degenerated. It became the fashion to put words into the mouths of the characters that were so distinctly ungrammatical, so totally out of phase with the legitimate comic counterparts, that it must have been intentional. Even illiterates could not have been guilty of such gross misuse of the language. This, too, helped divorce the erotic comic from any genuine association with reality. It probably added to the acceptability of the product.

The next great change took place when the characters began to cross their comic-strip borders. Joe Palooka might turn up warming the bed of Ella Cinders. Dick Tracy, penis rampant in the breeze, might be found in hot pursuit of a not-so-unwilling Daisy Mae. Perhaps the most imaginative examples of little "dirty" comics were produced during this phase, before the publishers decided that the sexual situations were more important than the characters depicted. Certainly, by eschewing the old bounds of legitimate comic strips, they gained a far wider scope for the erotic imagination.

And new characters were appearing whose characteristics lent themselves to even wilder sexual exploitation. Superman, able to leap tall buildings at a single bound, should be capable of sexual feats far beyond those performed by mere comic mortals. On the other hand, consider the possibilities inherent in a sex situation which revealed the Man of Steel to be a sexual dud. Frequently, in these strips, the smaller and meeker the character, the greater and more potent the organ with which the artist endowed him. Only Popeye seems to have survived as a sexual titan, and then only through the consumption of excessive quantities of spinach.

Real characters began to appear, joining the old comic personalities in their sexual adventures. These were usually the popular filmic idols of the day. And if they had reputations for sexual adventuring in real life, as did Mae West (who still does as this is written, carefully fostered by her life style), they might be paired with the most sexually potent of the original cartoon characters. Needless to say, the living individuals so lampooned generally were not too happy about their new representations, although few expressed any public sentiment on the matter. The disadvantages of that sort of publicity have saved many an eroticist from legal prosecution.

On occasion, the artists and publishers would invent their own characters, never seen on the pages of newspapers. Usually, these characters did not equal the genuine article in popularity, though they did permit new and more graphic or arcane situations.

There were times when other factors than character, situation or dialogue enlivened the proceedings in the "eight-pager." It was customary to run off a number of different comics at one time, and sometimes odd things happened in the binding process. Pages would be interchanged, and the reader would find pictures out of sequence or context. Such examples are particularly prized by modern collectors.

Other characteristics also changed during the evolution of the little dirty comics. The sexual activities depicted were, initially, restricted to coitus in various positions. The mores of the times militated against what were considered "deviant" sex acts, and the artists restricted their characters to those sexual actions which their readers might be willing to accept as normal. The necessary reader identification was thus retained.

Later, as competition for the existing market grew greater, more liberty was taken by the artists (we have seen the same trend in those erotic publications published currently for the adult market). Oral sex acts, such as fellatio and cunnilingus were introduced. (Even anal intercourse and homosexuality were depicted on rare occasions.)

It must be remembered that this was a period in which a man willing to perform cunnilingus was considered less male, an object of derision. The acts were often performed, of course, but there was no public acceptance of them. And only a whore would fellate a man—or so many believed. So introduction of oral sex to the "eight-pagers" marked a turning point. No longer did they provide only sexual humor. The titillation of the truly forbidden had been added. But they never approached in sexual strength the photographic representations available today.

The sexual limitations can be attributed to the fact that the artists, although they are considered by many as comparable with the underground artists of the present day, were neither in rebellion against the "establishment" nor particularly freer in their sexual attitudes than the general population of the period. It is a popular misconception that artists lead the way in sexual freedom. Actually, they generally prove neither more nor less advanced in this area than their fellows in other fields.

Another factor that tamed the sexual aspect of the earliest erotic comics was that they were not, in all likelihood, purely commercial ventures. There is excellent reason to believe that the idea began as a means of personal amusement, and that the instigators may have been the comic artists who invented the original, newspaper versions. This is borne out by what we know to have been very limited press runs on the earliest editions. Per-copy publishing costs are very high in limited editions; it is only when an extended press run is produced, with copies running into the many thousands, that commercial operations become possible. As no more than a hundred each of the earliest known versions appear to have been run off, it is possible that they may have been intended only for the private amusement of a close circle of friends.

Similar humor of a sexual nature is produced thusly in other areas of the entertainment and communications fields. The author, for example, knows of an extensive private collection of highly erotic radio and television commercials, produced in the same studios and at the same time as the versions later released for presentation to the public. One automobile commercial, produced for a major American manufacturer, is a classic well known in the industry. A complete script was written for the purpose by the writer of the original, "clean" version and, after the final "take" for the client, the complete cast assembled for the erotic version. It was filmed against the same background and with the same music. The same people went through their actions before the cameras and for the sound track; but what emerged on film will never titillate the imaginations of a television audience—and so far as is known, the automobile manufacturer that footed the bill has never "officially" learned of its existence. We suspect that something similar led to the production of the earliest little dirty comics.

Chapter Two

MASS PRODUCTION
FOR PSYCHOLOGICAL NEEDS

Unlike modern adult erotica, which is produced almost exclusively in the major cities of America, the little dirty comics were often the products of small town presses. The modern erotic magazine is big, slick, usually includes extensive use of high quality color illustrations. Its production demands the use of the most modern color laboratories, the latest high speed four-color presses, vast quantities of high grade and expensive paper and fleets of trucks to move it to the markets. The production of it is big business. It cannot be hidden from the authorities and, if it is to make its way safely in the commercial world, must depend on conformity with existing laws and to accepted business practices. This was not the case with the "eight-pagers" (*eight pagers* is a categorical term describing these books, although they frequently ran twelve or sixteen pages; they were also known as Tijuana bibles, although very few, so far as is known, were printed outside the United States).

The safest way to produce the little "dirty" comic book was under cover, at a printing plant already operating in a legitimate field. Sometimes this was done without the knowledge of the owner. It was a simple matter for the foreman, or anyone else holding a key to the establishment, to come in on a Saturday or Sunday, or on some evening when the press was not normally in operation, and run off a few thousand copies from a previously prepared set of plates. And so the "eight-pagers" originated, for the most part, in the smaller cities.

This was not always the case, of course. One of the few occasions on which the publisher of an erotic comic book was caught took place in New York, in 1935. The quantity confiscated was small, however, as the press run had just begun at the time of the raid. So far as we have been able to discover, charges against the publisher were never pressed.

As is the case with present day erotics, the largest consumption of little "dirty" comics was by "middle America," where the most sexually repressed are always found. The middle classes have always provided the greatest financial return to those who deal in sexually explicit material. And the erotic comics were brought to them by individual retailers, operating very much like present door-to-door salesmen. Selling his wares a few at a time to known regular purchasers, he could, on occasion, dispose of several thousand copies in the course of a month. As profits were high (as much as one dollar net profit per copy to the retailer) and the period was the depression, small fortunes were made by a few enterprising individuals.

But for most sellers of the "eight-pagers," profits were marginal, and the sale of this material was a sideline operation. A salesman dealing in some more legitimate product might carry a few dozen copies of the latest edition for a very few select customers.

Surprisingly, there is no evidence that the criminal element ever became involved in erotic comics production or distribution. The potential profits were there, had a concerted effort been made to organize an efficient method of manufacture and distribution. The cost of presses was small in comparison with the money that might have been made from them in continuous operation. Perhaps organized crime was busy with what it considered bigger things. Prohibition had not yet run its course. Prostitution on a large, commercial scale was in its heyday, and gambling operations then, as always, provided a steady income for the careful criminal. Erotic publications may not have been considered sufficiently lucrative. Ill-gotten gains could be better employed in other fields.

Eventually, competitive practices drove prices down, eventually ending all but a limited amount of production, for local consumption. But it was really a conglomeration of factors that ended the reign of the little "dirty" comic book.

Aided by the production necessitated by the greatest war in history, America climbed out of the Great Depression. And with economic recovery, societal standards changed. The nation became more liberal in its outlook, and that liberality extended into sexual matters. With greater public acceptance of explicit sexual material, the ill-drawn, often misshapen characters of the "eight pagers" no longer titillated the imaginations of America's middle-class male. Photographic renditions of sexual acts, far more graphic than the relatively innocent products of the comic artist's imagination, became more generally available. And the man who was really dedicated to the pursuit of erotica gradually lost interest in Jiggs, Moon Mullins, Smokey, and Betty Boop.

By the time the last days of the "eight-pager" rolled around, production levels and procedures were back where they had started from, in garage presses and attic binderies. Quality had deteriorated to the lowest level ever achieved in any printed publication. And artistic merit was totally an item of the past. The last publishers of erotic comics did little more than attempt to emulate, at lower cost, the actions depicted in the photographic erotica now gaining popularity. But art could not compete with technology. Even when they were presented at lower prices, the "eight-pagers" found few buyers. Once again, schoolboys were the principal purchasers.

The little dirty comics never entirely passed

from the American scene. Publication, although on a vastly diminished scale, continued through the war years and well into the postwar period. As late as the 1960s, it was possible to find new press runs in circulation, and not necessarily of the old established standards. The few artists still working in the field had kept abreast of legitimate comics, incorporating the new characters and situations. But the verve was gone. The true underground had been discovered, and the genuine talent was investigating new areas of sexual satire in cartoon form. And this time, it was genuine satire. A conglomeration of factors, ranging from the threat of nuclear disaster to ecological disaster had produced an entire subculture, totally alienated from that of their fathers. It was to this subculture that the new generation of artists was drawn.

Here and there, perhaps, a few elderly cartoonists still crouch over their drawingboards, delineating Popeye in all his rampant, penile glory. Somewhere, in the imagination of some tired artist, Betty Boop is about to have her kidneys tickled by Superman, or the Masked Marvel. The originals, however, have a flavor peculiar to the temper of the times in which they were published, and could never be completely faithfully reproduced—even by the most clever of the present-day artists. Here they are in all their absurdity and glory. Read them and laugh.

THE PRICE ON MANY OF THE COVERS OF LITTLE SEX COMICS, SUCH AS SEEN IN THIS EXAMPLE, OFTEN ACTED AS A BARGAINING POINT OF DEPARTURE, THE PEDDLER ULTIMATELY CHARGING WHAT HE THOUGHT THE TRAFFIC WOULD BEAR. IN ADDITION, FOREIGN PLACES OF PUBLICATION WERE OFTEN FICTIONALIZED TO CREATE AN IMAGE OF INTRIGUE.

A NIGHT IN PARIS

No. 306

PRICE, ONE DOLLAR

MADRID PUBLISHING CO.
MADRID, SPAIN

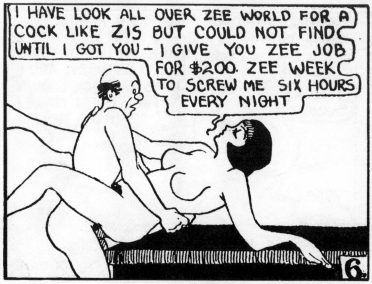

BECAUSE THE NAUGHTY COMICS WERE PRIMARILY DEPENDENT UPON THE PICTURE FOR THEIR EFFECT, THE VERBAL WAS KEPT AT A MINIMUM, AND ONLY AN AMOUNT SUFFICIENT TO FOLLOW A SIMPLE PLOT OUTLINE WAS EMPLOYED. IT IS FOR THIS REASON THAT "KISS ME AGAIN," WITH ITS UNUSUALLY LONG EXPOSITORY TEXT, REMAINS AN INTERESTING DEPARTURE FROM A CONVENTIONAL LITTLE "DIRTY" BOOK.

AFTER A FEW MINUTES OF SWAPPING EFFECTIONS HE HAD ME SITTING UP ON HIS DESK WITH MY DRESS UP OVER MY BELLY — AND HIS HAND BETWEEN MY LEGS, OF COURSE I PUT UP A LITTLE RESISTANCE JUST ENOUGH TO MAKE HIM THINK I WAS NO PUSH-OVER, BUT IF HE HAD PUSHED ME OVER THAT SECOND HE COULD HAVE DROVE IT HOME I WAS SO HOT, INSTEAD HE FONDLED AND PLAYED WITH MY BUBBIES FOR A WHILE AND THEN GAVE ME SOME MORE FINGER THIS TIME I SHOWED NO RESISTANCE, I COULDN'T IF I HAD TRIED —

AH COME ON KIDDO DON'TCHA LIKE ME JUST A WEENE'BIT—

YES, BUT MR. BIFF

SOON HE HAD HIS JOCK OUT AND WAS IT A JOCK I THOUGHT IT WAS A ROLLING PIN WITH THE HANDLES OFF, HE ASKED ME TO FEEL IT, I HESITATED FOR A MOMENT — THEN SEIZED IT AN BEGA RUBBING IT — IT WAS AS HARD AS A ROCK AN HOT AS HELL — IT GAVE A FEW THROBS AND I KNEW HE WAS READY FOR ACTION — JIMMIE, THAT IS HIS NAME, TOLD ME TO BEND OVER THE DESK AND HE WOULD TAKE IT TAKE IT FROM THE REAR — WELL HE TRIED TO PUT IT IN MY ASS HOLE - GOSH I FELT LIKE THE GRAF-ZEPPLIN TRYING TO ENTER

JIMMIE TO YOU BEAUTIFUL

OUCH THAT HURTS!

—SO I SAID TO HELL WITH THAT NOISE, SO I PULLED OFF MY DRESS TO KEEP IT FROM BEING SOILED AND LAY BACK ON THE DESK WITH MY ASS ON THE EDGE AND MY LEGS OVER HIS SHOULDERS— AND DID I GET FUCKED I MUST HAVE CAME 6 TIMES— DID HE KNOW HIS STROKES I THOUGHT MY PUSSY WAS GOING TO SPLIT— HE GAVE ONE HUGE PUSH AND GRUNT AND I FELT THAT HOT STUFF SHOOT INTO ME I WOULD HAVE SWORN I COULD TASTE IT IN MY MOUTH IT WAS SUCH A LOAD—

OH-H-JIMMIE-OH- I GOING TO COME, FUCK ME JIMMIE.!

WE WERE JUST LETTING IN SOAK FOR A FEW SECONDS WHEN THE DOOR OPENED AND IN WALKS THE BIG BOSS IT WAS THE FIRST TIME I HAD SEEN HIM AND HE SURE RAISED PLENTY OF HELL FOR THE NEXT FEW MINUTES— I THINK JIMMIE SHIT ON HIMSELF BECAUSE SOMETHING SURE SMELT BAD-WELL I WAS SO SCARED IT MIGHT HAVE BEEN ME! ANYWAY HE TELLS ME TO COME INTO HIS OFFICE AND AS FOR JIMMIE HE WAS FIRED—

—TH' BOSS.!

WHAT'S GOIN' ON HERE—

WELL I BEGAN TO LET THE OLD TEARS FLOW AND GIVE HIM THE OLD SOB STORY ABOUT SUPPORTING MY SICK MOTHER AND TEN BROTHERS AND SISTERS - AND THAT I HAD BEEN FORCED TO JAZZ JIMMIE TO HOLD MY JOB - WELL THE OLD BASTARD KINDA SOFTENED AND BEGAN ASKING ME QUESTIONS, I NOTICED HE KEPT GLANCING DOWN AT MY CUNT - I HADN'T HAD A CHANCE TO PUT ON MY DRESS - WELL I'M GLAD I HADN'T NOW -

H-M-M - SO YOU ARE A NEW GIRL, HERE, FROM OUT OF THE CITY

BOO HOO YES SIR

PRETTY SOON HE HAD ME SITTING ON HIS LAP PETTING ME LIKE A BABY - COOING NICE THINGS TO ME ONCE AND A WHILE HE WOULD PAT ME ON MY BARE LEGS AND KINDA HUG ME, I JUST KEPT ON SNIFFIN' - I KNEW THE OLD BASTARD HAD HOT NUTS CAUSE I COULD FEEL A HARD BUMP IN THE CRACK OF MY ASS - AFTER A FEW MINUTES HE HAD HIS HAND ON MY CUNT AND ONE ON MY TITS - I KINDA WIGGLED TO HELP HIM FINGER ME BETTER.

OH, MR. BLURP YOU MEAN YOU'RE NOT GOING TO FIRE ME -?

HEE-HEE - NO MY LITTLE GIRL I WOULDN'T DO A THING LIKE THAT!

THE FULLER BRUSH MAN

IN

"HOT PANTS"

I WAS ON MY WAY TO JACKSONVILLE AND TOOK THE BOAT OUT OF NEW YORK - THOSE BOATS ARE A HOOKER'S PARADISE AND THE FIRST TIME I SAT DOWN ON DECK A TEMPTING DAMSEL APPROACHED ME ——— 1.

2.

THE FOLLOWING "HOT NUTS" COMIC REPRESENTS AN EARLY DE-
PARTURE FROM THE USUAL FORMAT BOOKLETS, WITH ITS TWENTY-
FOUR PAGE SPREAD AND ITS TEN-DOLLAR PRICE TAG.

OUR SUSIE WAS A "CORN-FED",
AWAY BACK ON THE FARM —
WHERE SHE HIT THE HAY AT SEVEN
AND WAS FAR AWAY FROM HARM.

HER DADDY HIRED A FARM-HAND,

TO PLAY NURSE-MAID TO THE STOCK,

AND SUSIE STUMBLED UPON HIM

STROKING-THE-ROD BEHIND A ROCK.

SHE COULD'NT FORGET THE AWFUL SIGHT,

SHE THOUGHT OF IT NITE AND DAY,

WONDERING WHAT THAT THING WAS FOR,

SWORE SHE'D FIND OUT ANYWAY.

ONE DAY SHE FOUND HIM SWIMMING
IN THE POND WAY DOWN THE DELL,
THAT THING WAS DANGLING 'TWEEN HIS LEGS
SHE'D FEEL IT OR GO TO HELL.

SO SHE TOOK OFF ALL HER CLOTHING
AND LAID THEM ON THE ROCK,
DOVE INTO THE POND BESIDE HIM
AND GRABBED HIM BY THE JOCK.

THE YOKEL SOON GOT EXCITED,
BUT I ASK YOU - WOULD'NT YOU ?
HE THREW HER DOWN UPON THE BANK
AND STUCK IT UP HER FLUE.

SHE FUCKED THE POOR SAP SIMPLE,

HIS BALLS WERE HANGING LIMP,

SHE HAD HIM CUTTING PAPER-DOLLS,

HE WAS SOON A FUCKED-OUT-SIMP.

So Susie started out to fuck,
she couldn't get enough Peter.
She wasn't so hot at anything else
but at screwing they couldn't beat'er

SHE LAYED 'EM ANYWHERE AT ALL.

IN THE PARK OR IN THE STREET,

SHE FUCKED 'EM ON THE TOWN-HALL STEPS

WHEN THE COP WAS OFF THE BEAT.

SOON SHE HAD THE TOWN FUCKED SILLY,

BUT SHE WASN'T SATISFIED.

HER NUTS WERE OVERHEATED,

"I'LL FUCK OR DIE", SHE CRIED.

THE BOYS BEGAN TO AVOID HER,
THEY COULD'NT STAND THE PACE.
THERE WASN'T A HARD-ON IN THE TOWN,
NOT A FUCK IN THE WHOLE DAMN PLACE.

SO SHE PACKED UP HER BELONGINGS,

HOPPED A RATTLER IN QUEST OF PRICK,

SHE'D FUCK THE WORLD IF SHE HAD TO,

BUT SMALL PETERS MADE HER SICK.

SHE FUCKED EVERY BUM IN THE CITY,
BUT NONE OF THEM WOULD DO.
NOT ONE OF 'EM HAD COCK ENOUGH -
WHAT COULD THE POOR GIRL DO ?

SHE HUNG A SIGN UP ON THE DOOR
FOR A MAN WHO'D FUCK HER RIGHT,
OR FOR PRICKS OF ENORMOUS SIZES,
SHE WAS IN AN AWFUL PLIGHT.

THEY CAME AND WERE ALL FOUND WANTING
NOT A ONE OF THEM HIT THE SPOT,
BUT SUSIE JUST KEPT ON TRYING,
'CAUSE HER CUNT WAS PIPING HOT.

THEN SHE HAD AN INSPIRATION,
SHE'D TRY 'EM FUCKING DOUBLE.
BUT THAT EVEN FAILED TO PLEASE HER,
SHE SURELY WAS IN TROUBLE.

So she hunted up a sculptor,

Had him measure the size of her cunt,

Told him to mould a mammouth prick.

This would surely do the stunt.

IN GLEE SHE TRIED THE PRICK OF CLAY
AND COMMENCED TO DO HER STUFF,
BUT SOON DISCOVERED HER FOLLY
THE DAMNED THING WAS TOO ROUGH.

THEN THE SCULPTOR HAD A GOOD IDEA,

A WAX ONE WOULD DO THE TRICK.

SO HE WENT TO WORK IN EARNEST,

MADE A GORGEOUS WAXEN PRICK.

BRIGHT AND EARLY SHE CALLED TO GET IT,
IT WAS READY THE VERY NEXT DAY,
BUT HER CUNT WAS OF SUCH TEMPERATURE
THE DAMNED THING MELTED AWAY —

THE POOR KID WAS SAD AND DISTRACTED,
'TIL THE CIRCUS CAME THAT WEEK —
THEN SUSIE FOUND HER PARADISE,
NO FURTHER HAD SHE TO SEEK.

23

SUSIE ADVISES ALL HER SISTREN,
IF THEY CAN'T FIND PRICK ENOUGH —
JUST JOIN OUT WITH A CIRCUS
AND LET THE ELEPHANT DO HIS STUFF.

THE PROVERBIAL FULLER BRUSH MAN, THE POPULAR DOOR-TO-DOOR SALESMAN IN THE THIRTIES WHO BECAME THE SUBJECT OF COUNTLESS JOKES SURROUNDING MIDDLE AMERICA'S FEAR OF THE DISSOLUTION OF THE FAMILY UNIT, WAS INCORPORATED INTO AN ADVENTURE SERIES OF INNUMERABLE "EIGHT-PAGERS."

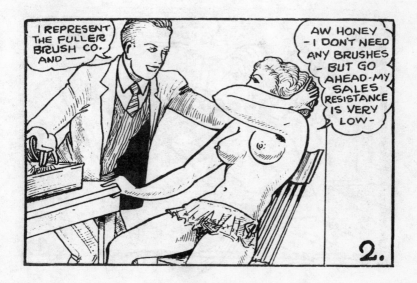

THESE LITTLE "EIGHT-PAGERS" REPRESENT MORE THAN JUST COMIC RENDITIONS OF "DIRTY" STORIES. THEY ARE REFLECTIONS OF THE STYLES, MANNERS, AND ATTITUDES OF A BYGONE AGE. THE CHARACTERIZATIONS AND ART WORK OF THE FOLLOWING OPHELIA PRATTE CAPER PLACES THIS COLLECTOR'S ITEM WELL INTO THE EARLY THIRTIES.

Ophelia Pratte

IN

Selling Subscriptions

THE COVERS OF MANY "EIGHT-PAGERS" CONTAINED LITTLE OR NO ILLUSTRATED MATERIAL AND RATHER INNOCUOUS TITLES, SUCH AS "THE OPEN ROAD," "HELP WANTED," AND "FIRST AID." IN CONTRAST, THE FOLLOWING COVER DEPICTING BEAUREGUARD GOOSEOIL WITH A GARGANTUAN APPENDAGE TYPIFIES A LARGE NUMBER OF SEX COMICS DESIGNED TO GUARANTEE THE READER OF THEIR LECHEROUS CONTENT.

FOR MANY YOUNG MEN AND WOMEN, THE "EIGHT-PAGER" WAS THEIR FIRST INTRODUCTION TO THE HUMOROUS AND THE LUDICROUS IN SEXUAL ACTS. THE VISION OF ADMINISTERING TO THE WOUNDED GENITALIA OF A "CONNIE CLAPP" ENLIVENED THE LIBIDO OF MANY A BOY, AND HARMED HIS ID NOT ONE WHIT.

WITH THE INFLUX AND THE POPULARITY OF THE PULP LOVE MAGAZINES AND THE "SOAP OPERAS" OF THE FORTIES, THE LITTLE "DIRTY" LOVE STORY APPEARED ON THE SCENE TO KEEP PACE WITH THE CHANGING REQUIREMENTS OF THE READING PUBLIC. THIS UNUSUALLY LONG "FORTY-EIGHT PAGER" EXEMPLIFIES THE LITTLE "DIRTY" LOVE STORY.

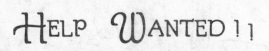

HELP WANTED ! !

SATURDAY AFTERNOON...

SHE'S NUTTY AS A PECAN GROVE· WANTS TO RIDE IN THE COUNTRY· BUT SPENDS MOST TH' TIME STANDING THERE THINKING· WISH SHE WEREN'T SO ALOOF· I'D SHOW HER A HELLUVA BETTER TIME!

26

ARTHUR, HAVE YOU HAD ANY EXPERIENCE IN MASSAGE? IF YOU HAVE, WHAT KIND?

YES· I'VE LEARNED MANY TYPES· AROUND GYMS AND TOO, BEING A CHAUFFEUR, IT'S BEEN EXTRA DUTY WITH RICH EMPLOYERS

TONIGHT I'LL ARRANGE FOR US TO BE ALONE· NOT EVEN A MAID· SO WE WON'T BE EMBARRASED BY INTRUSIONS, AND YOU CAN ATTEND ME UNMOLESTED· I'VE ALWAYS HAD MY MASSAGE BY WOMEN· LATELY I'VE FELT CRAMPS· AND I FEEL A MAN'S EFFORTS WOULD GET BETTER RESULTS.

27

SATURDAY NIGHT...

HERE'S A SMOCK· I'LL BE WITH YOU SOON, MY BATH IS WAITING

28

HOLY SMOKE, SHE DOESN'T REALIZE THAT MIRROW IS THERE! - OR DOES SHE? CRIPES! - I CAIN'T STAND THIS MUCH LONGER!!!

29

AND WHAT ARTHUR SEES IS MOST EXCITING!!!

30

PART OF THE POPULARITY OF THE LITTLE SEX BOOKS, SUCH AS THIS FULLER BRUSH MAN COMIC WAS THAT THE READER COULD ENJOY THE TOTALLY LUDICROUS STORY-LINE WITHOUT GETTING INVOLVED IN A SITUATION WHERE HE COULD IDENTIFY WITH THE CENTRAL CHARACTER. AND THEY WERE GENUINELY FUNNY.

FORESKIN CUNTWELL IN "GRANDPA'S REVENGE" IS AN EX-
AMPLE OF THE TYPE OF SEX COMICS WHICH WERE PRODUCED FOL-
LOWING THE SECOND WORLD WAR. THE THIRTY-TWO PAGE FORMAT
WAS ONE OF THE WAYS PROMOTERS EXPERIMENTED IN AN EFFORT
TO REVIVE A DWINDLING MARKET THAT WAS NEVER TO RETURN TO
ITS PEAK DURING THE GOLDEN AGE OF THE "LITTLE" DIRTY COMICS.

ONE DAY I WAS SITTING IN MY OFFICE READING ONE OF MY LATEST BOOKS WHEN THERE WAS A KNOCK AT MY DOOR. *1*

OF COURSE THIS PISSED ME OFF CAUSE I WAS JUST GETTING A NICE BIG HARD-ON AND SURE DIDN'T LIKE THE IDEA *2* OF BEING INTERUPTED.

AND THERE BEFORE MY EYES STOOD AN OLD JAG-OFF COLONEL FROM THE SOUTH, ALL PISSED OFF AT ME BECAUSE I'VE BEEN WRITING ABOUT THE SOUTH. 3

HE WAS REALLY MAD, BUT I COULDN'T TALK TO HIM (AFTER ALL, I LAYED MANY A SOUTHERN BELLE IN MY DAY.) SO I DUCKED BEHIND MY DESK. 4

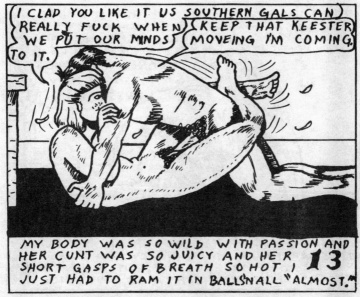

BOY I NEVER THOUGHT THIS BLACK PUSSY COULD BE SO NICE AND JUICY WHEN I WAS WRITING ABOUT IT IN MY BOOKS.

AS WE FELL TO THE FLOOR I FELT HER COME BEFORE WE HIT AND THEN I REALLY DROVE IT HOME SHE LOVED IT AND SO DID I. 23

WHY MR. CUNTWELL YOU SHOULD KNOW BETTER. YOU SHOULD KNOW US BLACK GALS CAN REALLY FUCK WHEN THE TIME COMES

WELL I'M GETTIN' HOT PANTS JUST WATCHIN' HOW ABOUT ME GETTIN' A LITTLE FUCKIN'

I HEARD HER BITCH ABOUT WANTING FUCKED BUT I DIDN'T PAY ANY ATTENTION THAT BLACK ASS WAS TO HEAVENLY TO THINK ABOUT ANYTHING ELSE. 24

125

COME ON SAM WAKE UP AND GIVE ME A LITTLE FUCKIN!

WHY SURE I WAS JUST DREAMING ABOUT HOW I'VE WANTED TO FUCK YOU SINCE I'VE COME TO WORK FOR YOUR GRAND PAPPY.

I HEARD THE SPRING SQUEAK AS SHE JUMPED INTO BED AND GRABED SAMS PRICK. SOON THEY BOTH BREATHING PASSIONATELY AS THEY FUCKED FIERCELY. **27**

WHY SAM IF I'D A KNOWN YOU COULD FUCK LIKE THIS I'D A FUCKED YOU LONG AGO.

MY GAL BUT YOU GOT A LOVELY PUSSY IT SURE WAS WORTH WAITING FOR.

AFTER A FEW RUSTY LOADS WERE EXCHANGED IN GLORIOUS FUCKIN' THE TWO OF THEM CAME BACK INTO OUR ROOM AND **28** CONTINUED.

HERE! HERE! WHAT'S THIS ALL ABOUT.

WHY GRAND PA I'M JUST SHOWING FORESKIN SOME REAL SOUTHERN HOSPITALITY.

HE WALKED OVER TO WHERE WE WERE FUCKIN' LIKE MAD AND YELLED SHE TRIED TO EXPLAIN AS BEST SHE COULD, BUT IT WASN'T NESSESARY 'CAUSE HE SAID ----

31

SOUTHERN HOSPITALITY HUMP! GET THAT MAN'S COLD BALLS OFF THE GROUND ROLL THAT ASS THATS WHAT I CALL SOUTHERN HOSPITALITY.

YES, GRANDPA DEAR.

GRANDPA'S CHANGE OF HEART WAS SOON EXPLAINED, CAUSE HE PUSHED ME ASSIDE AND SLIPPED HER THE PRICK HIMSELF. SO I WENT HOME WITH PLENTY MATERIAL FOR MY NEW BOOK

32

THE PUBLISHERS OF SEXY LITTLE COMICS WERE INTERESTED IN ONLY ONE THING—MONEY—AND THEY TRAVELED FAR AND WIDE IN THE REALMS OF LITERATURE AND HISTORY FOR THEIR SUBJECT MATTER. IN THIS JESSE JAMES CLASSIC, THE BACKROOM ARTIST UTILIZED THE AMERICAN WEST. IN THIS CASE, HOWEVER, THE INDIAN MAKES A "HORSE'S ASS" OUT OF THE WHITE MAN.

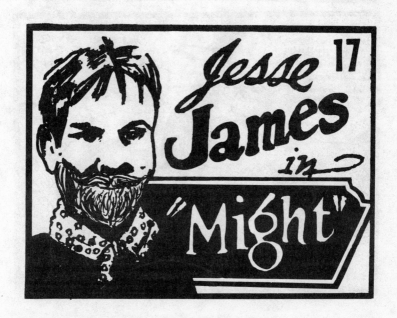

133

TO FULLY UNDERSTAND THE APPEAL OF THE "DIRTY" COMICS, ONE MUST STUDY THEM IN THE LIGHT OF THE ERA IN WHICH THEY WERE PRODUCED. THE TWENTIES AND THIRTIES, IT MUST BE REMEMBERED, WAS A TIME OF SEXUAL REPRESSION, AND THE PURCHASE OF A BOOBS BOOKLET INDICATED A HEALTHY REBELLION OF A SIGNIFICANT PROPORTION OF THE AMERICAN PUBLIC.

2.

BOOBS WAS RAISED ON A FARM IN
WEST HUCKLEBERRY, IOWA WHERE SHE
GREW UP TO PLAY NURSE-MAID TO A LOT
OF COWS AND CHICKENS — SHE NEVER
LEARNED WHAT THAT HAIR-POCKET WAS
INTENDED FOR 'TIL A TRAVELING SALESMAN
STOPPED AT THE FARM HOUSE ONE NIGHT
AND SHE'S DREAMED OF IT EVER SINCE —

THIS RURAL RACKET AND SHE DECIDED
TO VENTURE FORTH INTO THE COLD, CRUEL
WORLD — WHILE TAKING HER BATH SHE
PERUSED THE LOCAL BELLYACHE AND
CAME UPON A WANT AD THAT SEEMED
TO BE JUST THE TOPS — SHE HAD ENOUGH
GEETUS TO REACH CHICAGO AND THERE
WAS A MID-NITE TRAIN OUT OF HUCKLEBERRY.

SO BOOBS PACKED HER FEW BELONGINGS
IN A SHOE BOX, WRAPPED THE CAT AROUND
HER NECK, PULLED UP HER STOCKINGS AND
FLITTED THROUGH THE BARNYARD — SHE
KISSED THE PIGS GOOD-BYE AS SHE WENT
FLITTING————————————
YES, DEAR READER OUR HEROINE HAS
EMBARKED — WHAT WILL IT LEAD TO ?

AFTER MUCH WANDERING BOOBS
FINALLY LOCATED THE BROWN RUBBER
EMPORIUM — NOT A VERY IMPOSING PLACE
BUT WHAT THE HELL — A JOB'S A JOB AND
BESIDES BOOBS IS AFFLICTED WITH A
VERY BAD HABIT OF EATING — AND IF BOOBS
DON'T MAKE SOME CABBAGE SHE CAN'T EAT
AND IF SHE DON'T EAT SHE WON'T SHIT AND
IF SHE DON'T SHIT SHE'LL DIE ——

THE GUY POUNDED AWAY LIKE A MAD-MAN AND ALTHOUGH BOOBS SORT OF ENJOYED IT SHE HAD BUSINESS TO ATTEND TO—

BOOBS HAS RUNG THE BELL FOUR TIMES BUT HE CLAIMS THE THING HASN'T REALLY GOT HARD YET—

OUT IN THE COLD AGAIN !! AND THE
FIRST DAY ON THE JOB — BUT BOOBS
HAS FOUND WHAT SHE WANTED, PROVING
THE OLD BROMIDE "SEEK, AND THOU SHALL
FIND" — AND — IF IT'S A LITTLE SCRATCHING
YOUR HUNTING FOR, JUST DRAG DOWN
YOUR DRAWERS

THE RADIO SALESMAN IS AN EXAMPLE OF THE TYPE OF SEX COMIC DEVOTED PRIMARILY TO THE PRESENTATION OF AS MUCH SEXUAL CONTENT AS POSSIBLE WITHOUT ANY COMPLICATION OF PLOT. IT DOESN'T FOLLOW THE PATTERN OF A CONCLUDING PUNCH LINE OR TWIST ENDING. NOR DOES IT RELY ON ANY CONFLICT, SUSPENSE, OR DENOUEMENT. ITS SOLE PURPOSE APPEARS TO BE THE DEPICTION OF SEXUAL EXCITEMENT TOWARD THE ORGASM ON THE FINAL PAGE.

151

THE PRICE OF A LITTLE "DIRTY" COMIC BOOK IS NOW MANY TIMES HIGHER THAN THAT WHICH THE LOCAL PURVEYOR CHARGED THIRTY YEARS AGO. KANSAS CITY KITTY, WITH ITS FAIR ATTENTION TO DETAIL AND ITS SEPARATE EXPOSITORY FRAMES, RANKS HIGH AMONG MANY COLLECTORS.

HE PRESSED HIS LIPS TO MINE AND HIS TONGUE WENT INTO MY MOUTH AND I DID THE SAME AN I WAS CERTAINLY IN A HEAVEN OF PLEASURE HE PUT HIS FINGER FAR INTO MY CUNT, I REACHED DOWN GRASPED HIS HUGE PRICK, HIS BALLS WERE NICE AND LARGE AND I JUGGLED THEM AROUND IN THE SACK, FROM THE HARDNESS AND THE JUMP-INESS OF BOB'S PRICK I KNEW HE WAS READY AND WAITING TO FUCK ME, AND I, DESIREING IT AS HE DID PRESSED MY BARE BELLY ON HIS PRICK AND I THOUGHT I WOULD BREAK IT.

OH BOB DEAR I CAN'T WAIT ANY LONGER — I'M AFIRE — OH BOB-B-B ——

ARE YOU TELLING ME — SMACK— SMACK—

FINALLY BOB GENTLY EASED ME DOWN UPON MY BACK AND PLACED HIMSELF BETWEEN MY WIDELY SPREAD THIGHS I HAD NO FEAR AT ALL OF HIM HURTING ME — AND TAKING HIS LOVELY PRICK IN MY HAND AND GIVING IT A FEW SQUEEZE I STEERED IT STRAIGHT TOWARD THE MOUTH OF MY BURNING CUNT AS HE SLOWLY LET HIS BODY LOWER ON MINE AND LET HIS PRICK SLOWLY INTO ME, I FELT A THRILL SPINNING THROUGH ME

WELL HERE SHE GOES — ATTA GIRL — BOY WHAT A HOT SPOT — U-M-M

I WRAPPED MY LEGS AROUND HIS BACK AND WIGGLED UNDER HIM LIKE A REAL OLD TIMER — OH IT WAS CERTAINLY GRAND THAT FIRST FUCK I BELIEVE WE KEPT IT UP FOR OVER A HALF A HOUR HE INCREASED HIS MOVEMENTS AND I FELT MYSELF COMING, MY CUNT OPENED AND CLOSED LIKE A HAND SQUEEZING ON HIS PRICK THEN I FELT A LOAD OF SOMETHING HOT SHOOTING INTO ME — AND THEN I KNEW HE HAD SHOT OFF IN ME—

BOB-OH-H-BOB— I COMING-O-H-H BOY—OH—BOB O-H-H-H-H-H

3

PUSHING HIM OFF ME I JUMPED UP AND STARTED TO CRY AS I FELT THAT HOT STUFF RUNNING DOWN MY THIGHS, OH BOB I CRIED WHY DID YOU SHOOT INSIDE OF ME LIKE THAT. I CANNOT HAVE A BABY I WILL BE RUINED DISGRACED AND I CRIED SOME MORE,. HE LAUGH-ED," YOU'RE O.K. DEAR I SLIPPED A PILL IN THERE BEFORE I STARTED TO DO IT TO YOU, IT WOULD BE IMPOSSIBLE FOR YOU TO BE CAUGHT IN TEN LOADS, THAT RELEIVED ME TO SOME EXTENT, I RAN INTO THE BATH ROOM THE STUFF STILL CASCADING DOWN MY LEGS—

OH BOB WHY DID YOU DO IT — OH-H- BOO-HOO— HOO-HOO-

WHAT TH'HELL'S TH' MATTER

4

WHEN I RETURNED I FOUND BOB WATCHING BETTY AND JACK, JACK WAS ON TOP OF BETTY HER CLOTHES UP IN THE AIR AND JACK WAS TRYING TO GET HIS PRICK INTO HER BUT HE WAS JUST DRUNK ENOUGH TO MISS THE HOLE EVERY TIME, AND SHE DID NOT KNOW ENOUGH TO GRAB HIS PRICK AND STEER IT INTO THE HOLE, I BAWLED BOB OUT AND TOLD HIM TO HELP JACK OUT INSTEAD OF STAND--ING THERE LAUGHING AT THEM. — DO IT YOUR SELF HE LAUGHED—

HA-HA HA HA!!

HIC' SWING YER' ASS AROUND HIC' TH' DERN THING WON'T HIT TH' HOLE-DAMMIT-!

OHHH-N

5

— AND I, NOT AT ALL ADVERSE TO FEELING THE STALWART PRICK OF JACK, I TOOK A FIRM HOLD OF IT, AND NOT WITHOUT A FEW SQUEEZES ON MY OWN PART, I OPENED BETTY'S CUNT AND PLACING THE HEAD WITHIN ALLOWED HIM TO RUN IT UP INTO HER -THEN BOB AND I WATCH--ED THEM, THEY BOUNCED AND DANCED ON THE BED AND JACK SURE GAVE MY FRIEND BETTY A ROYAL FUCK, I THOUGHT HE WAS GOING TO BORE A HOLE IN HER THE WAY HE PUSHED AND POUNDED

NOW PUSH — PUSH, I'LL GUIDE IT!

THANX-OL'PAL' I'LL STEER YOU SHOME TIME HIC'

6

FINALLY I SAW HER EYE LIDS FLUTTER AND HE GAVE ONE DRIVE UP IN HER AND A TERRIBLE GRUNT AND I KNEW BY THEIR ACTIONS THAT HE WAS SOAKING HER THE SAME AS BOB HAD DONE TO ME, AFTER A MINUTE OR TWO JACK ROLLED OFF HER, AND SHE LAY ON THE BED LIKE DEAD HER DRESS ALL OPEN SO THAT YOU COULD SEE HER CUNT AND IT WAS ALL RED AND OPEN AND LOOKED WET AND SEEING THAT WHITE STUFF RUNNING DOWN HER LEGS —

WHOOPS! SHAKE YER ASS BABY PAPA'S GOING TO FLOOD YER BOWLES

7

I DIDN'T THINK BETTY HAD TAKEN ANY PILL OR ANYTHING SO I HALF DRAGGED AND CARRIED HER TO THE BATH ROOM AND SET HER ON THE TOILET SEAT AND WASHED THE LOAD OUT OF HER CUNT., WE SAW BOB AND JACK SEVERAL TIMES THE FOLLOWING WEEK BUT NOTHING WAS SAID OF WHAT HAD TAKEN PLACE THAT NIGHT AT THE APT. — HOWEVER BOB PHONED US AND ASKED US HOW WE WOULD LIKE TO GO ON A REAL WILD PARTY — WOULD WE? WHAT DO YOU THINK.

WELL IF YOU DON'T LIKE IT - HIC' YOU CAN KISH MY ASS —

THE END

8

OFTEN THE COMICS BECAME VEHICLES OF SATIRE AND SOCIAL COMMENTARY ON CONTEMPORARY ATTITUDES AND BEHAVIOR. THIS FULLER BRUSH MAN ADVENTURE, PRESENTED IN THE FORM OF EDUCATIONAL MATERIAL, SATIRIZES THE POPULAR MARRIAGE MANUALS OF THE TIME DOWN TO THE CLASSIFICATION BY TITLE OF EACH INTERCOURSE POSITION. WHAT BETTER MEANS OF LAMPOONING THE MARRIAGE MANUAL THAN THE IRONIC EMPLOYMENT OF THE POTENTIAL "HOME WRECKER," THE FULLER BRUSH MAN, AS THE INSTRUCTOR ON COITUS?

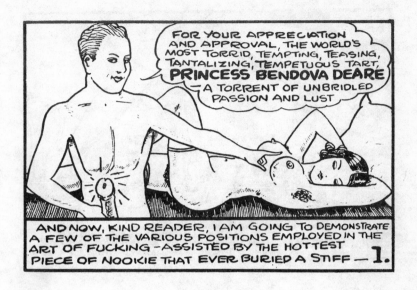

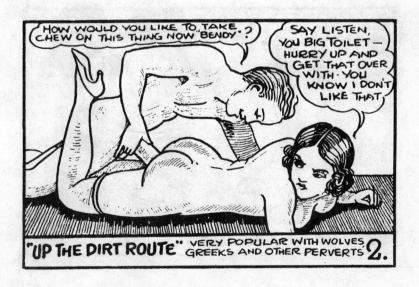

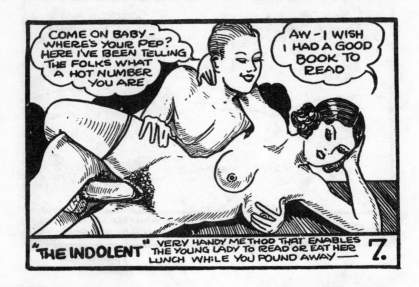

LAPPO AND DILDO DOOLEY (PAGE 170) ILLUSTRATE THE EM-
PLOYMENT OF A CONCLUDING SITUATION COMMON TO NUMEROUS
"EIGHT-PAGERS"—THE HUMOROUS YET EMBARRASSING PREDICA-
MENT OF "BEING CAUGHT IN THE ACT." WHILE THE MAJORITY OF
SEX COMICS CONCLUDED WITH A HUMOROUS PUNCH LINE, AS IN
DILDO DOOLEY, LAPPO DEPARTS FROM THIS TRADITION BY MAKING
THE HUMOR OF THE EMBARRASSING SITUATION ALONE SUFFICE.

166

THE MALES IN MOST OF THE SEX COMICS WERE NOT DEPICTED AS SEXUALLY PROVOCATIVE HEROES, ALTHOUGH THEIR FEATS AND APPENDAGES OFTEN REACHED HEROIC PROPORTIONS. THEY WERE USUALLY LUDICROUS FIGURES, FREQUENTLY SHORT, FAT, HOMELY, "SIMPLE SIMON" TYPES. DILDO DOOLEY IS A CASE IN POINT. THE CONCLUDING PUNCH LINE OF THE CHEATING WIFE TO HER HUSBAND, "I BET YOU'LL THINK I'M AN AWFUL FLIRT," ENDED MANY AN "EIGHT-PAGER" IN IDENTICAL OR SIMILAR FORM.

THIS "FRIGIDAIRE SALESMAN" (NOT TO BE CONFUSED WITH THE UBIQUITOUS "FULLER BRUSH MAN") COMIC IS UNUSUAL FOR SEVERAL REASONS. IT UTILIZES THE LITERARY DEVICE OF THE FLASHBACK, A RARE TECHNIQUE FOR THIS GENRE, AND IT ALSO MAKES USE OF THE CINEMATIC DEVICE OF THE CLOSE-UP SHOT, EVEN MORE RARE. BUT THE COLLECTOR WILL VALUE IT MOST OF ALL FOR THE DESIGN OF THE FRAME, REMINISCENT OF NINETEENTH CENTURY LITHOGRAPH EDGINGS.

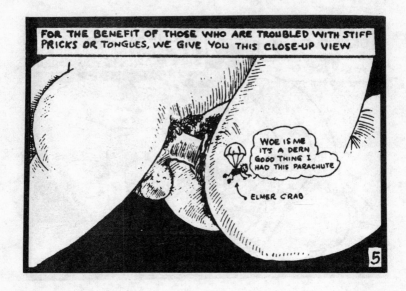

MISS ANNIBELLE

IN

"DRINK UP"

"COW SHED FRUIT FIZZ"   3.

"A LITTLE CORDIAL"   4.

"MAIDEN'S DREAM" 5.

"TOM & JERRY" 6.

"A PICK-ME-UP" 7.

"OLD FASHIONED" 8.

ALL WAS NOT HEAVEN FOR THE HEROES OF SEX COMICS, AS THIS PIERRE LA DOUCHE BOOKLET DEMONSTRATES. THE MALE'S FEAR OF FUMBLING IN THE BEDROOM AND THE FRUSTRATIONS OF A SEXUALLY REPRESSED SOCIETY WERE OFTEN TARGETS OF SATIRE AND SOCIAL COMMENTARY.

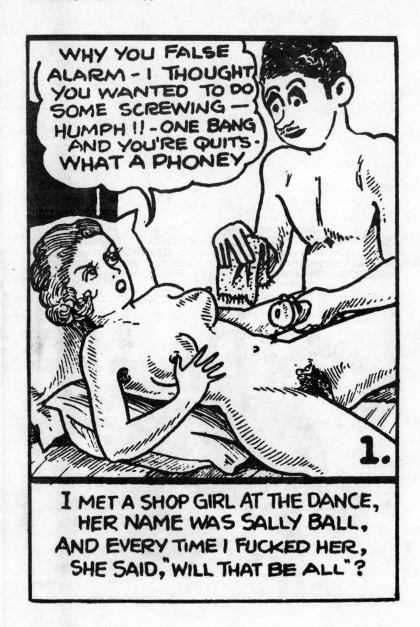

THE GIRL I HATE
    IS GOLD TOOTH MINNIE;
LOTSA HEY, NONNIE NONNIE
    BUT NO NINNIE NINNIE.

Chapter Three

REFLECTIONS OF
CHANGING ATTITUDES

That men and women will no longer pay a significant part of their weekly incomes for a few pages of bad drawings, depicting comic book characters engaging in tame sexual acts, does not mean either that a market no longer exists for such material or that the erotic cartoonist will vanish from the American scene. On the contrary, to a few collectors of the rare and the unusual, *genuine* early little "dirty" comics are items of great value, comparatively. And as for the artists, a new generation of them is portraying, in publications selling for pennies on newsstands around the country, human and bestial sexual antics that would have shocked to the core of their beings those artists who introduced erotic cartoons to the American scene.

While new efforts in the old style will probably have little commercial appeal, the originals —such as those used in the production of this volume—have become almost priceless gems of "camp" art. They represent, together with those used in earlier publications and with those as yet unused, one of the major collections of an art form that almost died unnoticed. But the changing American attitude toward sexuality made possible their resurrection. What we once considered the height of obscenity is now quaint.

We stated earlier in this volume that it was photography which killed the little "dirty" comics, but that is only partially true. The fact is, they simply failed to evolve in a changing world. So now we are concerned only with their history and with the effect they had on the generation that witnessed their flowering and decline.

That they served a genuine purpose cannot be questioned. Had they not been desired or needed, no market of any consequence would have been found for them. And even those who opposed them most strongly must have recognized their importance and, possibly unconsciously, been aware of the need for them. The police methods of the time, if fully applied, could have removed them from the scene. School authorities could have kept them from the hands of students. True, they were confiscated from time to time, but we suspect that those occasions were prompted more by a desire for them by teachers than the belief that they were damaging to the students. In any event, punishment for possession of the little dirty comics in the classroom seldom consisted of anything more than confiscation—and on more than one occasion that we know of, the confiscated copies were soon being passed from hand to hand among the teachers.

At the height of their popularity, the erotic comics far exceeded in circulation any of the currently available erotic publications. Publication ran into the millions. Foreign language editions were shipped to other countries. They were far more commonly found in the hands of youngsters than are their descendants, the slick erotic magazines of the present. Yet *Playboy* is less commonly found among the effects of today's teenagers than were the "eight-pagers" of yesteryear; and this despite the far higher price of the older literary and artistic erotic endeavors. In the nineteen thirties, a good Dagwood and Blondie "dirty" comic might cost as much as two dollars. This could easily have represented more than half a day's pay for a man who supported a family—and yet these booklets found their way into the hands of high school students who considered a dime big money. For eight to sixteen pages of crude, black-and-white drawings, they were willing to spend what was then important money. On a comparative basis, taking into consideration such matters as variety of sexual acts displayed and total number of different acts pictured, the five-dollar erotic magazine of the present day would have represented a value, in those times, of several hundred dollars.

Why were the men of the thirties willing to pay so high a price for so poor a product? The answer must lie in the humor inherent in those ancient comics and the temper of the times in which they were sold. Only those who can remember the days of the great depression can fully appreciate the affluence of the present. Just getting enough to barely live on, from day to day, was impossible for many. Anything that could provide a few moments of humor was clutched at in a world that seemed destined to descend into the blackest level of total depression. It seemed, in those days, that the downward slide would never end. In times like that, men grasp at whatever will take their minds off reality.

So the manufacturers and purveyors of the little dirty comics prospered. Their market was anxious to buy every product that came off their presses, and the authorities were interested in only feeble attempts to suppress the trade. Indeed, there is every reason to believe that they only went through the motions of acting against the publication and selling of the "eight-pagers" for the sake of appearances. *Beyond the few confiscations mentioned earlier in this volume, there is no case that has come to our attention of a publisher or seller being prosecuted on any charge relating to these little books.* Arrests there may have been, but matters were, apparently, never carried beyond that point.

Of course, we must take into consideration the fact, known to almost all, that the police of that day were far more prone to accept gratuities and look the other way, but they could not have done so to such a degree had there not been at least a tacit approval of the erotic comics by the authorities. Perhaps they were more enlightened in their own way than present law enforcement authorities. Perhaps, after reading a few samples themselves, they realized that the language used in them and the actions expressed were not too far removed from their own ways. It must be remembered, that this was a time in which prostitution flourished openly, when the neighborhood bootlegger was a respected businessman, and when everyone gambled openly through local bookies and numbers operators. In many ways, it was a far more permissive society than our own.

True, public morals were stricter. The double standard still held sway. Overt sexuality was not acceptable in public. But there was also far less governmental control on behavior, or on what the public could be subjected to. Ministers might thunder from the pulpit about the evils of pornography, waving copies of the little "dirty" comics at their quaking congregations, but it was expected that the parents of wayward children who read these "evil" works would apply the necessary pressures. Few thought of having government, either on a local or a national level, take action against the publishers and purveyors.

This was a period less than halfway back in time to the days when drugs could be sold legally across the counter of the neighborhood pharmacy. Marijuana was not the great bugaboo that destroyed the lives of all who came in contact with it. And although it had been known to many and been used widely, it was not proscribed by national authority until 1937. In a period when hard narcotics were simple to obtain and marijuana could be smoked openly and legally on the public streets, it is not hard to understand the reluctance of any governmental body, local, regional or national, to take a stand against so commonplace and popular an item as an erotic comic book.

So they pervaded every aspect of American life. Those who opposed them may have deplored their popularity, but they were largely unable to do much about their beliefs.

Legitimate cartoonists probably constituted the strongest single force opposed to the little "dirty" comics. An artist is not necessarily amused when someone takes the fruits of his labors, the children of his imagination, and utterly destroys their original intent by subjecting them to sexual absurdities. Many of those early and great cartoonists considered their products to be socially significant. We can imagine the wrath in certain quarters when the first erotic Little Orphan Annie appeared, complete with a Daddy Warbucks far more devoted to the area between a lady's legs than to the saving of the world from unnamed forces of evil.

Of course, as previously stated, a few of the earliest "eight-pagers" may well have been produced by the same hands that penned the legitimate originals. Particularly in the case of the less widely syndicated cartoons, the artist's income might have permitted only the barest living comforts, and this was not a time of generally high incomes. The thirty, forty or fifty dollars per week such a man might receive for the deliberate perversion of his brainchild could represent, to him, a considerable sum of money. And if the publisher who employed him in the moonlighting operation produced dirty comics devoted to other popular characters, he could have the double satisfaction of dragging his competitors into the erotic marketplace.

It was the publishers, of course, who made the fortunes. At the height of the period, production cost of a single copy of a little dirty comic could not have exceeded two cents. This included press time, paper, ink, payment to the cartoonist and general overhead (this figure did not, necessarily, include any possible payments to local authorities; no records were kept regarding such matters, for obvious reasons). The publisher sold his product to those who distributed it for as much as fifty cents per copy. When it is realized that some publishers, over a period of years, printed many millions of copies of these works, it becomes obvious that major sums, even by present standards, were involved. And yet, we have no records today relating who these men were, or what became of the fortunes they made. Who knows what present great publishing empires were built on the profits from little "dirty" comics. Had law enforcement authorities taken a serious interest in these publications, this would not be the situation.

It is interesting to speculate on the personal motives of the adults who purchased the "eight-pagers" regularly. Some motives become obvious in the period when film stars began to replace comic characters in the little "dirty" comics. Hero worship is no respecter of individuals in any class of society, and film fans were probably far more common than they are today. The matinee idols of the period were adored not only by the youths of the period, but also by their parents. And many a man probably spent his money regularly and surreptitiously to observe the antic involvement of Mae West with Wimpy and Popeye.

And how did these really expensive (by the standards of the times) little books pass on into the hands of the younger generation? Did fathers pass them on to their sons as a part of the sex education program? If so, we never were the recipient of any such favors. Those copies of the little "dirty" comics this author encountered in those times were either gained through barter or purchased outright for hard cash saved carefully over an extended period of time. On several occasions, when the word was out that a particularly daring edition had reached the local retailer, some of us would pool our funds for the purchase of a new copy. Needless to say, we squabbled endlessly over who should have first crack at its pages.

In recollection, one remembers never being questioned by either parent as to possible possession of these works. They must have known of their existence, but not considered the matter of any great importance. Perhaps the average parent of the period considered an interest in erotic comics a normal part of the growing-up process. If this really was the attitude, it was a healthy one.

Girls, too, took an interest in their pages, although their reactions were not the same as the boys (the outward result of the double standard conditioning process?). The girls would giggle and blush, or with pseudonaivete ask what the words and pictures meant.

It is undoubted that a great many of the little

"dirty" comics served as masturbatory aids. Erotic pictures have always served this purpose, probably since the days of our Cro-Magnon forebears and earlier. They also served, again to our recollection, as aids to seduction. Many an avid youth, too bashful to make anything resembling an erotic suggestion to any real, live girl, regardless of what her neighborhood reputation might be, could nevertheless summon up sufficient courage to hand her a copy of Snuffy Smith's latest antics and await the reaction.

Not all the "dirty" little comics were professionally produced, even in the late thirties, when production was at its height. Again through personal knowledge, we can relate an incident in which an enterprising high school student was inspired to a height of artistic fancy by the example of the "eight-pager." The boy was young, thirteen, but biologically, emotionally and intellectually advanced for his years. He determined to personally improve on the commercial product and, for a period of some months, produced a one-sheet newspaper on a weekly basis, in which the better known teachers and students were reduced to cartoon caricatures of themselves and subjected to all the sexual indignities of which an advanced, thirteen-year-old mind is capable. Copies were sold to fellow students at high rates, although we doubt that a real profit was made, due to the limited production (only carbon copies were produced, and quality suffered accordingly). The publication, although produced on a weekly basis, was entitled the *Daily Tower*. Above the headline stood an erect penis, with lightning radiating outward from the glans. The rest of the issue (one page, printed on one side only) was devoted to cartoon representations of the aforementioned teachers and students, engaged in varied sexual acts with each other. As some of the scenes depicted known relationships between specific teachers, an intensive effort was made by the school authorities to find the culprit, but he hid his identity successfully. Undoubtedly, a copy of one of his ancient "newspapers" would be a valued collectors' item today.

We can assume that similar efforts, of greater or lesser artistic merit, were commonplace in other schools and areas. Children can be inventive, particularly when their minds are challenged simultaneously with the stirring of their libidos.

Not all the "eight-pagers" were as hard core, sexually, as those presented in this volume. There did exist a market for weaker material, which could be produced more openly and at even lower cost. These little books, using the same characters (often even more badly drawn), but in embarrassing, rather than explicitly sexual, situations, enjoyed a brief vogue at five to ten cents, among the high school students of the day. The appearance of sexually stronger material, despite its higher price, soon drove the weaker books from the market.

If the "dirty" little comics were so popular—receiving little opposition from the moralists and having so great an effect on so many other aspects of our culture—why did they pass from the scene? Why did they lose their grip on the imagination of young America? The answer is simple. They failed to change in a period of amazingly rapid social evolution. Complacent publishers, believing that they had a gold mine that would never fail, locked themselves into the concept that what had sold before would continue to sell in the future.

When sales started to slacken, they believed that the answer was to pump more "eight-pagers" into the market, to invent new titles, new characters, to make the action stronger and the characters more direct. Also, by this time, they may have believed that their investments were too heavy to risk any new approaches. So like the dinosaurs of old, they passed from the scene.

America had grown up during the lifespan of the erotic comic book. We entered the depression—and the era of the little "dirty" comic—convinced that fate alone had pulled the economic rug out from under the greatest nation in the world. We emerged from that same depression at the cost of the greatest bloodletting the world has ever known, and with the realization that we and our nation were mortal.

We were more sophisticated, intellectually and sociosexually. Whereas the First World War had exposed relatively few Americans to the reality of Europe and its culture, and the culture of the Far East, Americans by the many millions came back from the second great war with full knowledge that there was another world out there, with different and older standards than our own. Suddenly, the little dirty comics were puerile.

Sexually, we demanded stronger fare than second-rate artists could provide in the way of inferior, black-and-white line drawings—or we asked for nothing at all in the way of erotica but demanded the sexual freedom necessary to experience directly all that those old comics had depicted. Instead of the infantile dialogue emitted by the two-dimensional drawings, we needed reality, expressed as people speak—and act. The "eight-pagers" were children's fare to us. Where once they made grown men think erotic thoughts —then hurry home to their wives or girl friends— they now produced nothing but mild amusement. The magic was gone from them.

Where once a style in art could endure unchanged for centuries, the world was moving at a faster pace. And we were change conscious. The new, the different, was valued just for the sake of change. Originality, whether good or bad, was better than the best even the recent past had to offer. The rate of change had been accelerated by the war past all imaginings.

And our children were changing, too, at an even faster rate. It is not at all unusual for an emerging generation to doubt those values their parents held dear. This has always been a natural part of the human experience. Scholars have written of it since writing was invented. But never before, in Americans' experience, had the alienation between the generations been so great. And this alienation, too, had its effect on the erotica that amused us, when we, too, were a rebelling generation.

Show a modern seventeen-year-old a copy of a Dixie Dugan little dirty comic, and all he may see is a drawing of meaningless and unknown characters, performing hasty sexual rituals to the music of inane conversation.

And the action will probably be far tamer than that which he experiences on almost a daily basis. The youth of our nation are now sexually free—at least many of them are, and the rest are not far behind. It is not for nothing that millions of mothers across the land are having their physicians prescribe birth control pills and devices for daughters barely into their teens.

Long before the current crop of overtly sexual erotica appeared on the scene, genuine art books became available to the general public, and the "eight-pager" couldn't stand the pace. It was discovered by calculating publishers (perhaps some of them got their starts through printing little "dirty" comics?) that many of the great painters through the ages had known lighter moments while wielding their brushes. In addition to the paintings of places and people that had made their reputations, they had also turned out quite a few blatantly sexual works. That these existed had been known, until then, only by those fortunate few who held them in private collections, or to those museum curators who made a practice of inspecting the stuff all such institutions have in their basements, material generally considered too strong to place before the eye of the public. Then the aforementioned publishers discovered them.

While it was considered both illegal and immoral to sell, openly, cheap paperbacks and magazines illustrated with these erotic works, it was quite proper to print them on expensive paper and bind them between hard and expensive covers—then sell the product at a fancy price. It was art, after all, and no one but a prude could object to the dispensing of culture to those who had the bread to pay for it. So the man or woman who could afford to shell out fifteen or twenty dollars for pictures of people doing wild and wonderful sexual things to each other had access to all the fancies imagined by the erotic comic artists, but rendered by the hands of masters in full and glorious color. And he was acquiring culture, after all, not snickering over what that dirty old satyr in the picture was doing to the fair young maiden. Or was he? Little "dirty" comics or big, slick art; the effect is the same, if that is what the viewer wants. Not every subscriber to *National Geographic* buys the magazine for the sake of the pictures of pretty flowers, rare animals and far away scenic vistas. They still run an occasional article about primitive peoples who don't think much about wearing clothing in public. So it probably was and is with most of the art books sold.

The increasing availability of this sort of material, and the increasing ability of the average man to pay for it, left the "eight-pager" falling further and further behind in popularity. And another ingredient, lacking entirely in the little "dirty" comics, was increasingly in demand.

There is violence in today's erotic comics, something we never found in the old "eight-pagers." Their characters were innocent of any truly evil intent. They were out for fun and games, not physical damage to their opponents (this is not entirely true; several of the later "eight-pagers" mixed gore with the sex, perhaps in the hope of attracting a mixed bag of readers). If anything was injured in them, it was the ego of the vanquished member in the sexual bout.

But today the violence is essential and the sex a secondary embellishment. Indeed, it sometimes appears that the sex is included only to add spice to the violence.

We were examining the other day one of the latest segments in a popular underground comic strip. The principal characters in this epic are a collection of lesbians, whose purpose it is to destroy all men, wherever and whenever they can get their hands on them. This particular sequence ended in a grand orgy scene, in which the male victims were being forced to perform cunnilingus on the female victors, while having their testes crushed in the iron grips of the ladies. This is not the sort of humor that would have gone over with regular readers of the "eight-pagers."

Obviously, the purpose of such "comics" is not to entertain. They are intended as social commentary. Their purpose is to educate, as the artists understand "education," and whether or not we agree with the artists who produce this material, we must admit that they often get their points across quite powerfully. Unlike their progenitors, the little "dirty" comics—without which the present versions might never have come into existence— they do have a strong effect on the behavior of their viewers.

Or did the little "dirty" comics affect us strongly? During the peak years of their production, even the "clean" comics were under attack as destructive to the minds of their young and impressionable readers. If the innocent antics of Jiggs and Andy Gump were capable of warping developing minds (the argument of the opposition), then what effect did the "dirty" comics have? After an interval of more than thirty-five years, perhaps we can begin to examine rationally their true effects.

Did early exposure to this really primitive, though sexually overt material produce a generation of perverts? Were the young men and women who grew up with the "eight-pagers" distorted in any way by them? The records of our mental and penal institutions say otherwise, and modern psychological thinking holds that nothing but benefits could have come from this early exposure to erotica. A study was recently conducted in Los Angeles, California, of individuals either jailed or otherwise institutionalized for sex crimes and other antisocial sex acts. This was done under the auspices of the President's Commission on Obscenity and Pornography. The study revealed that almost all of the subjects studied had been held back from exposure to erotica in childhood. They had experienced upbringings in which sexually explicit material was forbidden. When caught reading or viewing such material, they had been severely punished by their parents for their "sins." It appeared that early sexual knowledge, and not necessarily through direct experience, produced results diametrically opposed to those predicted by the moralists.

Other prominent men and women in the behavioral sciences have concurred. The general consensus today is that exposure to explicit sexual imagery is essential to the normal developement of the individual, regardless of sex. Without such exposure, the development of a rational attitude toward the eternal interaction between male and female is impossible. In simpler terms, by the time they reach puberty, it is best if boys and girls are at least relatively familiar with their respective genitalia, and how they go together.

So the "eight-pagers" served a useful purpose after all. They educated us, albeit inaccurately, in the ways of men and women together. And although they misinformed us as much as they educated us, we should be grateful that we had them.

But what of the future? Is the lighthearted erotic comic book of the recent past forever dead? In a world faced with possible destruction through a number of sources, can we ever return to the time when simple caricatures taught boys and girls that sex was fun, that our bodies were meant to be enjoyed? Perhaps we shall. Legally. And with the wholehearted approval of our leading educators.

CONCLUSION

For some time, there has been growing pressure for a sensible sex education program in our public schools. Something of this sort, and far stronger than anything yet attempted, was recommended by the previously mentioned President's Commission on Obscenity and Pornography. These men believed it essential to the mental health of the nation that all of our children (and most of our present adult population) be taught in depth the truth, as we know it, about sex.

Although considerable opposition has been generated against such programs, usually by do-gooders who believe that ignorance is preferable to knowledge and equate that same ignorance with morality, programs are going ahead in schools all across the land. Motion pictures are being produced that show the entire process by which a baby develops, from impregnation through to parturition. There are few children left of school age who still believe that the stork brings babies.

Teachers are being given special training in the administration of sex education courses, and parents are being urged to permit their children to attend. The great religious institutions, those same organizations which once fought bitterly against even the mention of sex education are now strongly supporting such courses. There is disagreement of course, among them. But the arguments now are over the best means of bringing the data to the children, not over whether or not we should.

True, there are also disagreements over specific content, but the principal protagonists are all in the same ballpark. They argue now over details, not over the main course.

And out of their arguing a curious concept is slowly emerging. They are beginning to believe that possibly words and diagrams are not enough. Something more realistic is required—and a few psychologists have made a suggestion that is beginning to meet with approval: "Why not," they say, "print comic books similar to those the children read every day. The characters could be the same or similar, but instead of their usual antics, they could engage in sexual acts. Nicely, of course."

Anyone want to bet on the future of the LITTLE "DIRTY" COMICS?

BIBLIOGRAPHY

Atkinson. Terence. *More Little "Dirty" Comics.* Volume Two. San Diego: Socio Library, 1971.

Beaumont, Charles. *Remember? Remember?* New York: MacMillan, 1963.

Berger, Arthur. *Li'l Abner.* New York: Twayne Co., 1969.

Boardman, Fon W. *America and the Jazz Age.* New York: Henry Z. Walck, 1968.

Churchill, Allen. *Remember When.* New York: Golden Press, 1967.

Cole, William. *Classic Cartoons: A Definitive Gallery.* New York: World Publishing Co., 1966.

Couperie, Pierre. *History of the Comic Strip.* New York: Crown Publishing Co., 1968.

Feiffer, Jules. *The Great Comic Book Heroes*. New York: Dial Press, 1965.

Gilmore, Donald H., Ph. D. *Sex and Censorship in the Visual Arts*. San Diego: Greenleaf, 1970.

Gray, Harold. *Arf: The Life and Hard Times of Little Orphan Annie*. New Rochelle, N.Y.: Arlington House, 1970.

Hennessy, Eileen B. *A History of the Comic Strip*. New York: Crown Publishing Co., 1968.

Hillier, Bevis. *Cartoons and Caricatures*. New York: Dutton Co., 1970.

Holt, R.E. *Little "Dirty" Comics*. San Diego: Socio Library, 1971.

Lynn, Kenneth S. *The Comic Tradition in America*. Garden City, N.Y.: Doubleday, 1958.

Parkinson, Robert E. "Carnal Comics," *Sexscope Magazine*, Volume One, Number Three; Volume One, Number Four.

Sprague, William Edwin. *Sex, Pornography, and the Law*. San Diego: Academy Press, 1970.

Teach, William. *Kiss, Screw, Pleasure, and Sex*. San Diego: Greenleaf, 1969.

White, David M., and Abel, Robert H. *The Funnies —An American Idiom*. London: Collier-Mac-Millan, 1963.

Willet, Allen. *These Top Cartoonists Tell How They Create America's Favorite Comics*. Fort Lauderdale, Fla: Allied Publications, Inc.